THE MUPPET SHOW* ANNUAL
PUBLISHED BY

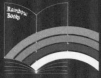

BROWN WATSON

A HOWARD & WYNDHAM COMPANY
135 WARDOUR STREET, LONDON W1, ENGLAND

MUPPET Characters
© Henson Associates, inc. 1956, 1976, 1978
*MUPPET SHOW and Character Names
are trademarks of Henson Associates. Inc.

PRINTED IN HOLLAND

£1·50p

The MUPPETS

PROUDLY PRESENT
YOUR MOST GENIAL HOST

 KERMIT THE FROG

THE DIVINE

MISS PIGGY

FABULOUS, FUNNY

FOZZIE BEAR

NUMEROUS GAMES & PUZZLES

 ROWLF

THE GREAT GONZO
AND HIS TAP-DANCING WALNUTS

STATLER AND WALDORF · PIGS IN SPACE

 DR. TEETH
AND THE ELECTRIC MAYHEM

Let's Welcome

Kermit

Despite the antics of his cast (including the determined attentions of Miss Piggy), this urbane, witty frog copes magnificently in the best theatrical tradition.

Miss Piggy

The vampish blonde bombshell, all woman in satin and pearls - UNTIL she's crossed! She is constantly seeking success with her two great loves - show business and a frog.

Rowlf

A gentle, philosophical observer of the changing (and often chaotic) scenes of life, his main ambition is to curl up with a piano and a good song.

Statler & Waldorf

They turn up religiously to enjoy hating the show-especially Fozzie. They enthusiastically berate everything, including each other, but obviously can't do without it all.

the Players...

Fozzie

This lovable earwiggling comic battles on through ruined routines and heckling from Statler and Waldorf, trying desperately to be funny amid the applause he never gets.

Gonzo

Ignoring repeated failures, Gonzo always manages to bounce back with even more fantastic plans for stardom, like singing prunes, yodelling clams and.....tap dancing walnuts!

Sam the Eagle

This very American eagle is the self-appointed guardian of moral standards, dignity and culture on the Show, although he doesn't know Nijinsky from Stravinsky.

Scooter

Kermit's tireless assistant is an important backstage organiser and character (especially as his uncle owns the theatre....) Scooter gives the star the "15 second" call.

Hi As compere and host of 'The Muppet Show', I'd like to welcome all of you to this, our second edition of 'The Muppet Show' Annual. I'm not actually very sure what annual means, but Sam tells me it has something to do with time and motion and steadiness of intent. What any of that has to do with this book, I don't know. Nor does Sam, who said that those were the very qualities missing from 'The Muppet Show' and that if this book was anything like our show, he didn't want anything to do with it.

We hope you have as much fun reading this (and none of the chaos) that we had putting it together. And I'd like to thank all of you for watching our show and reading our book – and I hope you have better luck with all the puzzles inside than we did, because Crazy Harry exploded most of them and Animal ran away with the rest. Oh yes,

and Gonzo has a great new act this year – Ted and Ginger, the tap-dancing walnuts!

Finally, on pain of ... well, on pain of whatever Miss Piggy finds that is suitably painful ... I have to tell all of you to ignore everything that comes before and after in this book and turn immediately to page 42 where you will find a wonderful, glamorous, beautiful portrait of Miss Piggy, who from now until eternity wants to be known, simply, as 'A STAR'.

Kermit the Frog

15

Monster Gallery

KERMIT'S MIND BENDER !

Kermit, being a Stage Manager, has to have a very good memory (though at times there's plenty he'd like to forget!) Now he's got a way to improve yours. Look hard at the picture below for about 2 minutes, then cover it up and make a list of all the things you remember.
Try it with your friends — the one who remembers the most is the winner!

※ AND REMEMBER.. NO PEEKING!

20

Spot the Difference

There are 10 differences between the two pictures below.
Answers on page 61. When you have spotted them, try your hand at colouring the second picture, using the top one as a guide.

The MUPPET TELLY RACE

SWITCH ON!

1
2
3
4
5
6 Rowlf. gets carried away by piano. Move to 11
7
8
9
10
11
12 Scooter gets on his scooter. Move on 5 spaces.
13
14
15
16
17 Waldorf falls through box! Move down to 27
18
19
20
21 Sam is struck by a sudden thought. Go back to 15
22
23
24
25
26 Crazy Harry blows a fuse! Miss a turn.
27
28
29
30
31
32 Sam censor's script Go back to 24
33
34
35
36
37
38
39 Kermit has to hide from Miss Piggy. Miss a turn.
40
41
42
43
44
45
46
47
48
49
50
51
52 Nigel (the conductor) gets on a bus. (Joke!) Move to 56
53
54
55
56
57
58
59
60
61 Statler falls asleep. Miss a turn!
62

SWITCH ON!

You know when you dash to switch on the T.V. when the Muppet Show is on? Well, here's a switched on race game... All you need is two or more players, a dice and counters. First to get through and switch on wins!

SWITCH ON!

1

2

3 Miss Piggy takes a short cut. Move to 8

4

5 Zoot blows a flat note Back to 2

6

7

8

9

10

11

12

13

14

15 Lucky you! Nip across to 21

16

17

18

19 Crazy Harry throws twice. You do the same!

20

21

22

23

24 Kermit falls down stage trapdoor. Miss a turn.

25

26

27

28

29

30

31

32

33

34

35

36

37

38 Animal blows up T.V. set. Go back to 32.

39

40

41

42

43

44

45 Gonzo on roller board. Move on to 51

46

47

48

49 Fozzie blows T.V. fuse! Back 5 places.

50

51

52

53

54

55 Gonzo falls asleep. Miss a turn.

56

57

58

59

61

62

MISS PIGGY'S PUZZLES

Miss Piggy has a few tricks up her sleeve, not to mention a savage right hook! That's because Kermit got the answers wrong. See if you can do better…

Here are a number of objects – Most are repeated but some are on their own. Can you spot them?

Miss Piggy thinks she's a match for anyone.
Now she's arranged fifteen matches to make five squares. Can you move three matches to leave three squares?

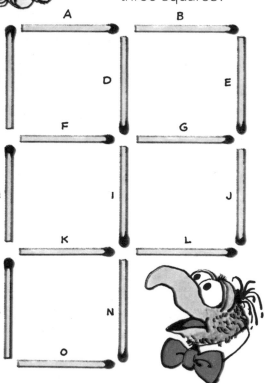

Answers on page 61

What's happening to whom?!

Something dotty is happening to someone dotty! But what is it?
Join up the dots and see. Then look at the answer below.

You're right!
Our Swedish Chef
has been making
pancakes. They
go up alright but
don't come down.
Trouble is, he used
self-raising flour!

Featuring Dr. Teeth-Keyboards and gravel vocals;
Floyd-Bassman; Janice-Left-hand guitar;
Zoot-Tenor Sax; Animal-Skins

The Great Gonzo's favourite snaps

"Great aren't they?"

Meet Fletcher...

and Robin in...

Hi kids! We thought that you would like to colour in
this page. You can find pictures of us in this book to help with the colours.

But who's in for a blast!

Crazy Harry is at it again—But who is in for a noisy surprise? Answer on page 61.

The Swedish Chef is chasing his chicky-chicky because he's dreaming of coq-au-vin. Can you help him to find her?

Rowlf
in Classical Mood

Annie Sue

A very talented and pretty young lady.
She sings like a bird, dances like a butterfly, and idolises Miss Piggy...
who is more than a little suspicious of her ambitions.

Kissy, kissy,
Miss Piggy
xx

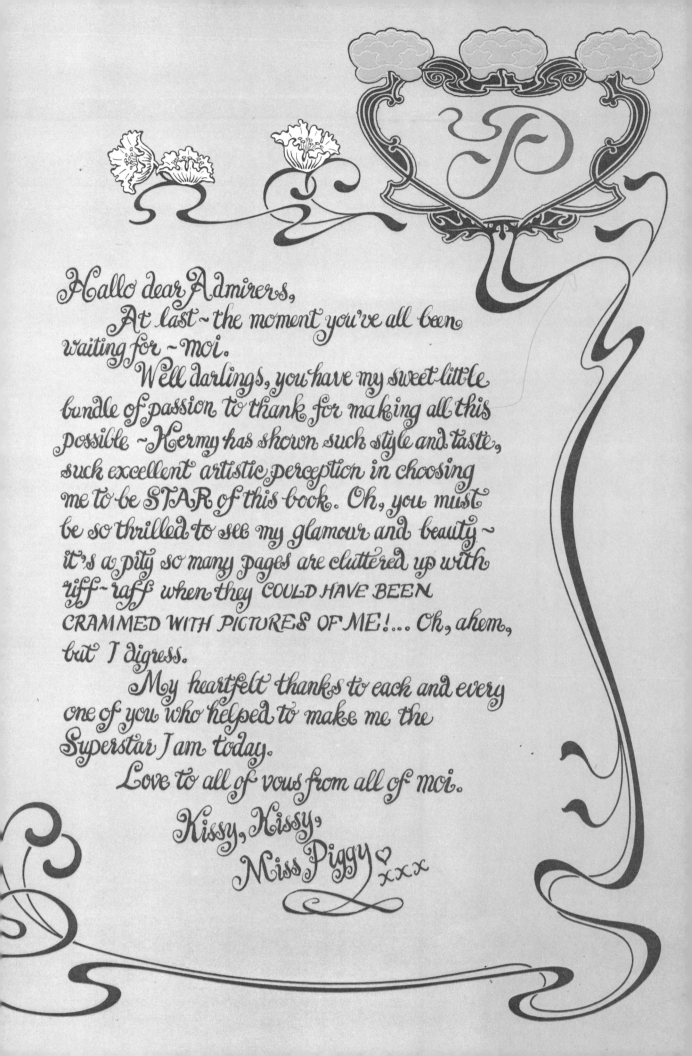

Hallo dear Admirers,

At last ~ the moment you've all been waiting for ~ moi.

Well darlings, you have my sweet little bundle of passion to thank for making all this possible ~ Kermy has shown such style and taste, such excellent artistic perception in choosing me to be STAR of this book. Oh, you must be so thrilled to see my glamour and beauty ~ it's a pity so many pages are cluttered up with riff ~ raff when they COULD HAVE BEEN CRAMMED WITH PICTURES OF ME!... Oh, ahem, but I digress.

My heartfelt thanks to each and every one of you who helped to make me the Superstar I am today.

Love to all of vous from all of moi.

Kissy, Kissy,

Miss Piggy ♡ xxx

DR. BUNSEN'S LABORATORY LARKS !

⭐ THE SAUCY STRAW!

Here's a little experiment from Dr. Bunsen's Lab., and unlike most of his experiments it does work (he hopes!) All you need is a drinking straw, sugar and soap.
Dip one end of straw into water and then into some sugar so that some of it clings to the inside of the straw.
Wipe off any left outside.

Then dip other end into bar of soap. Wipe outside.
Now float two pieces of matchstick in water. Touch water with soap end of straw between matches. They will move apart. Now do the same with the sugared end of the straw. The matches will be drawn together.

SOAP END   SUGAR END

BOBBING BUNSEN !

He obeys your commands!

Blow up an ordinary balloon, tie it, and with a felt pen, or paint, draw Dr Bunsen's face on it.
Then, on thin card, draw his boots.
The size will depend upon the size of balloon.
Cut out the boots and make a small hole, through which you pass the neck of the balloon.
And with the palm of your hand, making sure that it is dry, rub the balloon near the top.
This will give him a strange magnetism.
Point your finger at the spot you rubbed and he will bob towards you.
Move your finger away and he will bob back.
It'll puzzle your family and friends.

HOLE

edish Chef...and friend

Witchdoctor

Statler & Waldorf

Grosse

Beauregard

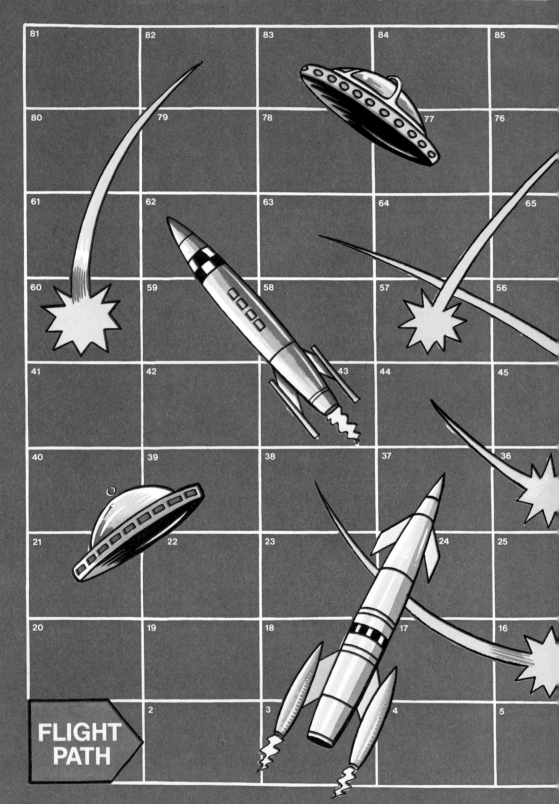

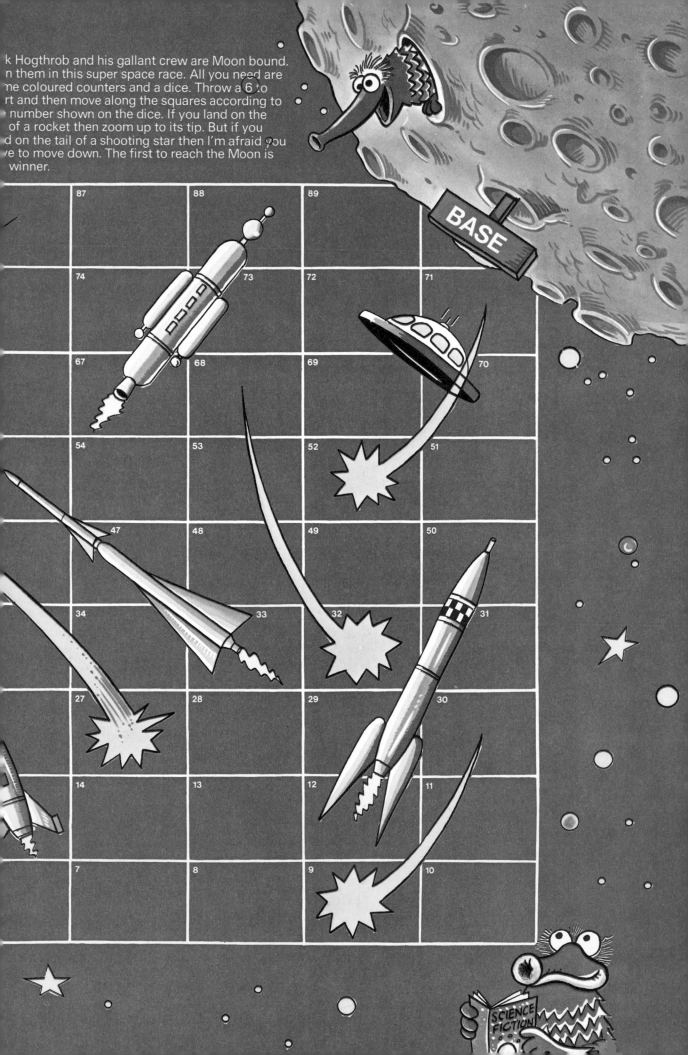

IPOVERLOL
LIVERPOOL

CESTNADOR
DONCASTER

NEEDUD
DUNDEE

BINDUREGH
EDINBURGH

RIFCAFD
CARDIF

DOFROX
OXFORD

SMOORTPUTH
SOUTHAMPTUN

CARSHENTEM
MANCH'STER

ROSTIBL
BRISTOL

"I'm sorry, I'll read that again..."

The Muppet Newsman sometimes gets tangled up in his tonsils! He mixed up the names of these British towns & cities, so help him out before the ceiling falls on him! Answers on page 61. You can also colour in the cartoon strip at the top of the page.

Crossword

The completed crossword grid:

		G		S	C	O	O	T	E	R
Z	O	O	T					I		
		N		K		C	H	E	F	
F	O	Z	Z	I	E		A			
	A	O		R		C	R	A	Z	Y
	N			M			R		S	
M	I	S	S	P	I	G	G	Y	T	
	M	U	E	T				S	A	M
	A	E				P		T		
F	L	O	Y	D		N	I	G	E	L
				I		I		L		
R	O	B	I	N	W	A	L	P	O	R	F

ACROSS

2) He says "15 seconds to curtain…" (7)
4) This Muppet plays saxophone (4)
6) Scandinavian Cook (4)
8) The fabulous furry funny man (6)
10) _____ Harry loves explosions (5)
12) She's the star, kissy kissy (4,5)
14) ____ The American eagle (3)
16) Dr Teeth's super cool bass player (5)
18) Unscramble "ELGIN" to find the Conductor of the Muppet Orchestra (5)
19) Kermit's nephew (5)
20) He sits in the box with Statler (7)

DOWN

1) He has a blue nose and bills himself as The Great _____ (5)
3) Fozzie wears this around his neck (3)
5) Your amphibious compere (6)
7) This crazy character is dynamite (see 10 across) (5)
9) Dr Teeth's mad drummer (6)
11) Waldorf's heckling companion (7)
13) Up-and-coming starlet, Annie ____ (3)
15) Miss Piggy thinks Link Hogthrob is a male chauvinist ___ (3)
17) Sam says the Electric Mayhem makes a terrible ____ (3)

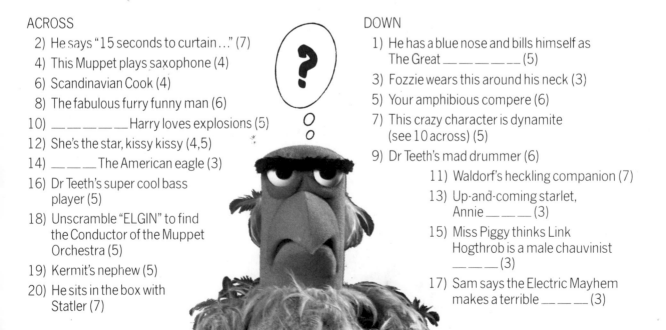

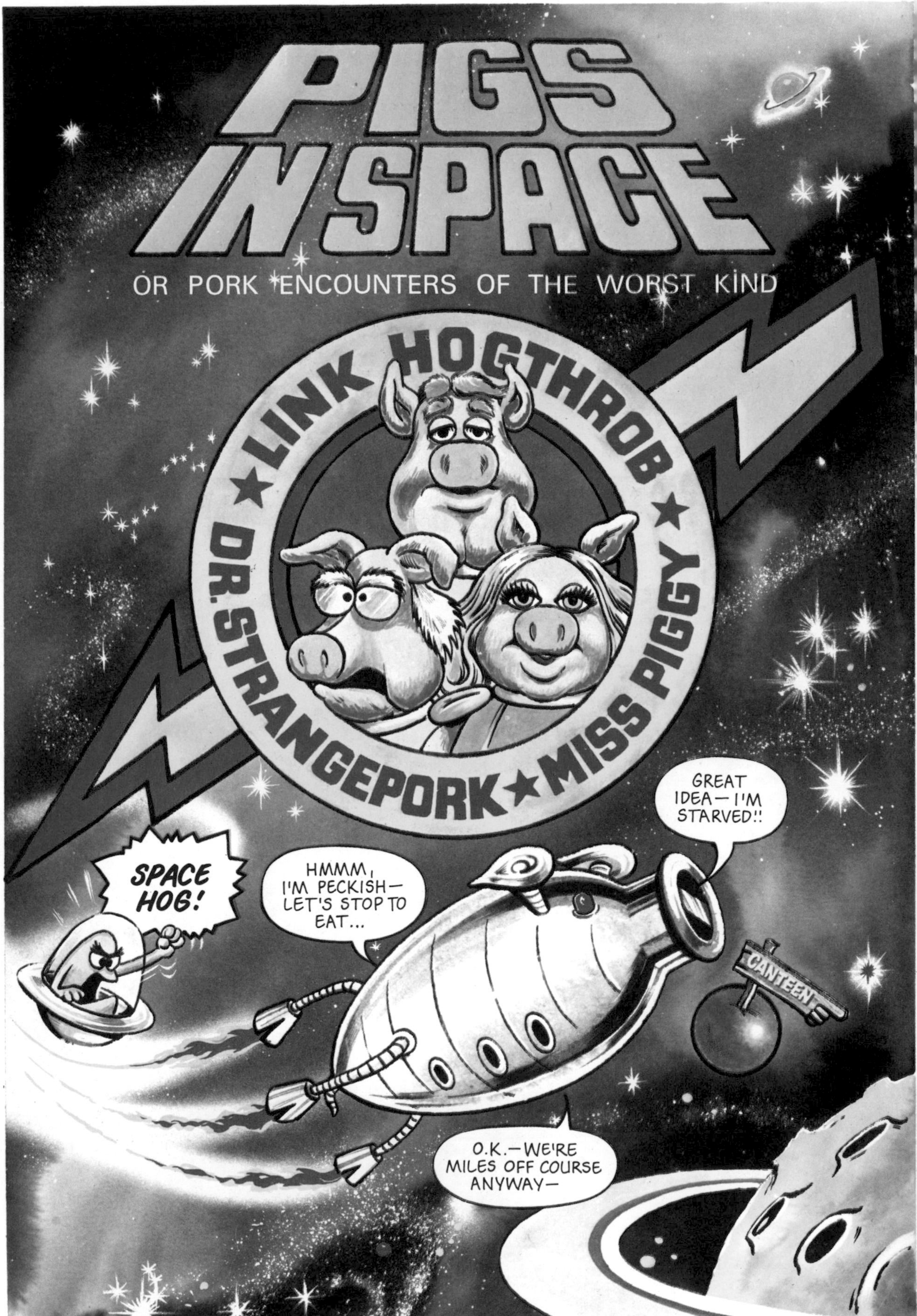
PIGS IN SPACE
OR PORK ENCOUNTERS OF THE WORST KIND
LINK HOGTHROB ★ MISS PIGGY ★ DR. STRANGEPORK
GREAT IDEA—I'M STARVED!!
SPACE HOG!
HMMM, I'M PECKISH—LET'S STOP TO EAT...
CANTEEN
O.K.—WE'RE MILES OFF COURSE ANYWAY—

52

54

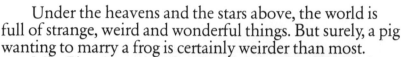

Under the heavens and the stars above, the world is full of strange, weird and wonderful things. But surely, a pig wanting to marry a frog is certainly weirder than most.

Miss Piggy's passion for Kermit burns on as brightly and as hopelessly as ever, but she is still no closer to her romantic dream – her wedding day.

The day she dreams of wearing a beautiful white dress with a long flowing train of lace, which has something old, something new, something borrowed and something <u>green</u>!

A bouquet of small pink roses, white lily-of-the-valley, fragrant yellow fresias and – aatishoo! Oh dear, just thinking about it has brought on Miss Piggy's hay fever! Where were we? Oh yes.

The day she hears her wonderful man ... er frog, say those magic words "I do", (sigh).

He slips that small band of gold on her left hand (if he forgot the ring she'd give him her <u>right</u> hand!). They walk together, she in a dream-like trance, from the altar ... the music plays, the choir is singing – probably off-key!

Smiling faces flank the aisle, blurred because she only has eyes for her beloved – in case he's looking at another woman!

Outside in the sun, they pose for the photographer on the steps. How strange they look – she two steps lower than he. The birds are singing, the chickens are squawking, monsters are throwing confetti – (I hope the meat-heads remember to take it out of the packet first!).

Dreamily she tosses her bouquet to the crowd ... Annie Sue misses it and Animal eats it!

Oh well!

It's all nonsense, of course, but all of us have dreams, so why shouldn't Piggy? The only difference is that hers is more impossible than most, but you can't help admiring her for trying so long and so hard to make it come true.

Maybe one day, Miss Piggy

ust a minute - the Knights are getting shorter!

GONZO   ZOOT

ONE OF THESE DRAWINGS
OF GONZO IS DIFFERENT
CAN YOU SPOT THE ODD ONE OUT ?

TWO OF THESE ZOOTS ARE ALIKE
CAN YOU SPOT THE PAIR ?

Answers on page 61

ANSWERS PAGE

PAGE 49 CROSSWORD ANSWERS

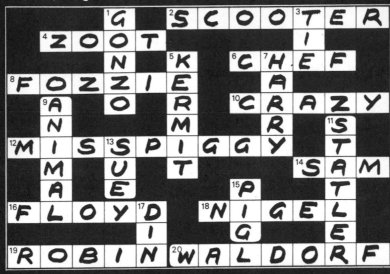

? BUNSEN RULES OK!

$$\sqrt[3]{\frac{x^3+y}{69}} =$$

$2+2=$

$2+2=4$ ✓

PAGE 21 – SPOT THE DIFFERENCE

1. MORE FLOWERS ON MISS PIGGY'S HAT.
2. LINES INSIDE MISS PIGGY'S EARS MISSING.
3. NECKLACE MISSING.
4. RING MISSING.
5. GLOVE SHORTENED.
6. KERMIT HAS THREE FINGERS INSTEAD OF FOUR.
7. POINT OF KERMIT'S COLLAR IS IN FRONT OF LEFT ARM.
8. KERMIT'S TONGUE MISSING.
9. FOZZIE'S NECKTIE IS DIFFERENT.
10. FOZZIE'S EYEBROWS ARE MISSING.

PAGE 24 – MISS PIGGY'S PUZZLES

SINGLE OBJECTS – FOOTBALL, SPECTACLES, PYRAMID.
MATCHSTICK PUZZLE – REMOVE B, E, H.

PAGE 39 – FOZZIE IS IN FOR A BLAST!

WOT?

$\pi r^2 = ?$

PAGE 48 – MUPPET NEWSMAN QUIZ

1. LIVERPOOL 2. DONCASTER 3. DUNDEE
4. EDINBURGH 5. CARDIFF 6. OXFORD
7. PORTSMOUTH 8. MANCHESTER 9. BRISTOL

PAGE 60

GONZO – ODD ONE OUT – "C"
ZOOT – 2 AND 3 ARE THE PAIR

I hope you got them all correct...
Bunsen